Gift Aid item

20 10015793 6028

NEW PIECES FOR TROMBONE

GRADES 3 – 6

© 1980 by The Associated Board of the Royal Schools of Music
14 Bedford Square, London WC1B 3JG

AB 1684

FOLK SONG

Andrew Byrne

SWINGING

Andrew Byrne

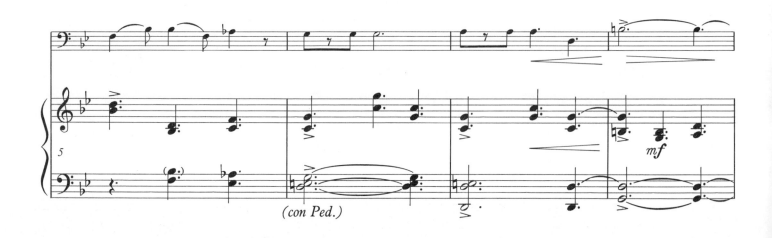

MOTHER CAREY'S GOOSE

Kenneth V. Jones

TRANQUIL TUNE

Terence Greaves

WALTZING AND MARCHING CHORALE

Terence Greaves

ORATION

Gordon Jacob

LAMENT

David Lyon

15

A.B. 1684

PRAELUDIUM

David Lyon

DANSE À LA RUSSE

Gordon Jacob

SACABUCHE

Kenneth V. Jones

MELODY

Richard Stoker

CONCERT PIECE

Richard Stoker

A.B. 1684 Printed in England by Caligraving Limited Thetford Norfolk